Seeds and Weeds

Copyright © 1978, Macdonald-Raintree, Inc.

Library of Congress Number: 77-27459

  2   3   4   5   6   7   8   9   0   82   81   80

Printed and bound in the United States of America.

Library of Congress Cataloging in Publication Data

Kirkpatrick, Rena K.
Look at seeds and weeds.

Includes index.
  SUMMARY: Easy-to-read text and illustrations
describe various kinds of seeds and weeds.

  1. Seeds — Juvenile literature. 2. Weeds — Juvenile
literature. [1. Seeds. 2. Weeds] I. King, Debbie.
II. Title.
QK661.W54   582'.0467   77-27459
ISBN 0-8393-0065-4 lib. bdg.

Look At
SEEDS and WEEDS

Words by Rena K. Kirkpatrick
Science Consultant

Pictures by Debbie King

Raintree Childrens Books
Milwaukee • Toronto • Melbourne • London

There are many seeds in our life.
Some seeds give us much of the food
we eat. Weeds grow from other seeds.

grapes

pears

cherries

lemons

oranges

All the foods on the table are fruits. They have seeds inside. Some have pits. When you break a pit open, you find the seed inside.

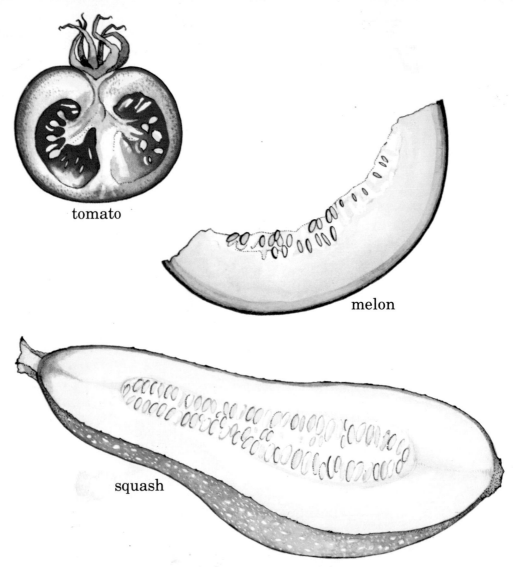

tomato

melon

squash

We eat the seeds of some foods. We eat tomato seeds. We do not eat squash or melon seeds. These foods have many seeds. A cherry has only one seed. It is inside a pit.

damp soil

plastic bag

rubber band

flower pot

soil

Seeds must be dried before they will grow. These children have dried the seeds. They will plant them in damp soil. The seeds are put just below the surface of the soil. The plastic bag helps keep the moisture from getting out.

1. Plant lots of seeds together.

2. Plant three seeds.

Two children did an experiment. In one pot they put lots of seeds. In another pot they put three seeds. They were both put in the same window for light. There will not be enough room in the first pot for all the plants to grow. They will not be strong and healthy.

We planted three squash seeds.
This is how they were planted.

The children tried another experiment. They wanted to know if it mattered which way a seed is planted. All three seeds will grow in the same way. They will all grow up out of the soil.

raspberry

gooseberry

strawberry

Here are three fruits. We eat the seeds of all of these. Gooseberry seeds are inside the fruit. Raspberries have many seeds. They are in each round part. Strawberry seeds are on the outside.

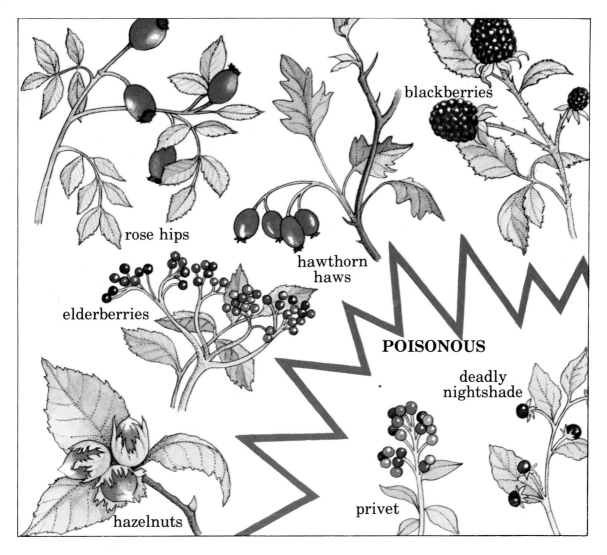

blackberries

rose hips

hawthorn haws

elderberries

POISONOUS

deadly nightshade

hazelnuts

privet

Here are two poisonous berries. People sometimes use privet plants as a hedge around a yard. The nightshade plant will grow under the hedge. The other plants shown are small trees or shrubs. The fruits can be eaten. Do not eat any berries or nuts unless you check with an adult.

In the spring people plant gardens. They also plant flower beds. Many stores sell the seeds. You may get a catalog delivered to your home. You can order seeds from this catalog.

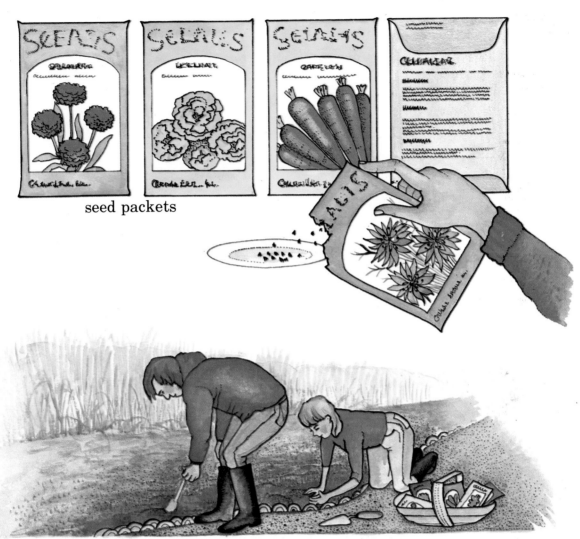

seed packets

These people are planting a garden. They are going to plant vegetables and flowers. Some plants grow for a long time before they have fruit. This is why people buy small tomato plants for a garden. You could start your own tomato seeds in the winter inside the house.

13

lid

saucer

water

plastic box

glass jar

pie pan

seeds on cotton

saucer

Mustard and watercress seeds grow quickly. We eat the new shoots. They do not need soil because they do not live long. They need water. The seeds are covered to keep them damp.

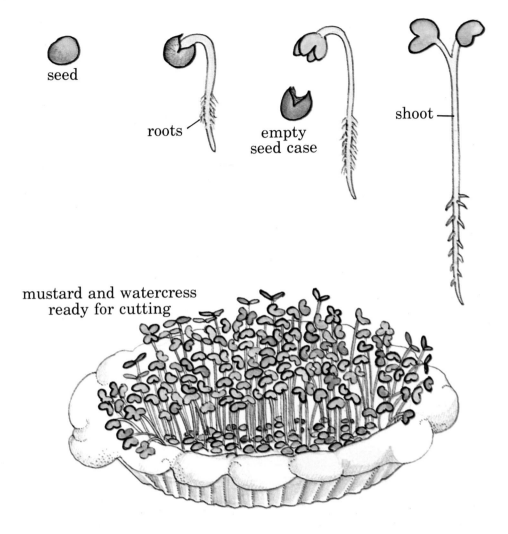

seed

roots

empty
seed case

shoot —

mustard and watercress
ready for cutting

In three or four days the roots will
appear. The empty seed cases will fall
off. Then you can see the shoots. They
will straighten up and grow. In about
a week you can cut the shoots.

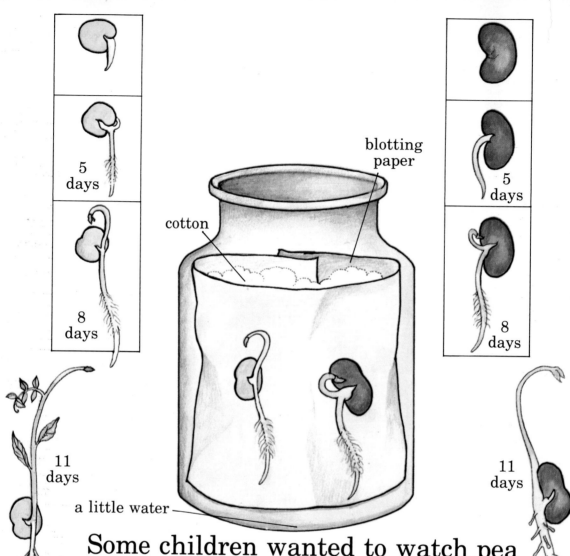

blotting
paper

cotton

5
days

8
days

11
days

a little water

5
days

8
days

11
days

Some children wanted to watch pea
and bean seeds grow. They put a little
water in the bottom of a jar. Blotting
paper soaks up the water. This will
keep the seeds damp. Cotton holds the
blotting paper in place. The children
watched the seeds for several days.
They will not live long because there
is no soil for food.

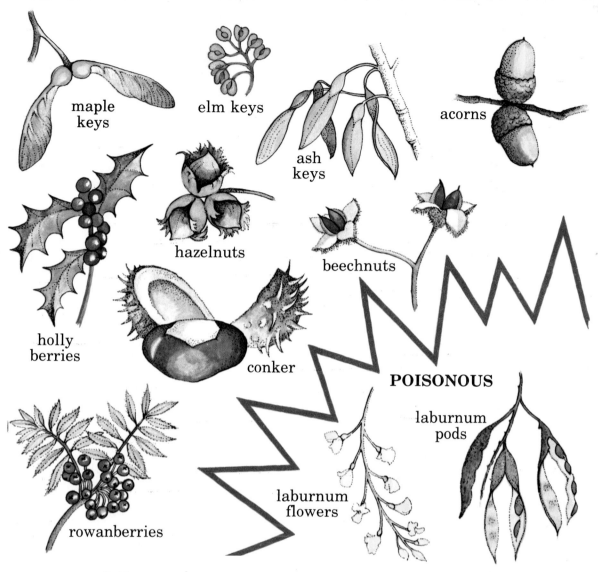

maple keys

elm keys

ash keys

acorns

holly berries

hazelnuts

beechnuts

conker

POISONOUS

laburnum pods

rowanberries

laburnum flowers

Many trees have fruits that are food for birds and animals. People eat the nuts from many trees. Some trees' flowers and fruits are poisonous. Be sure to ask before eating any fruit.

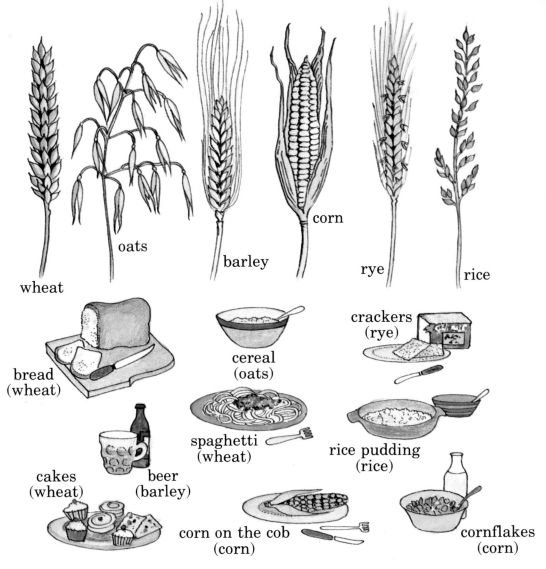

wheat

oats

barley

corn

rye

rice

bread
(wheat)

cereal
(oats)

crackers
(rye)

cakes
(wheat)

beer
(barley)

spaghetti
(wheat)

rice pudding
(rice)

corn on the cob
(corn)

cornflakes
(corn)

The seeds of some grasses are used for food. We call them grains. Farm animals eat these grains. We eat them in many different foods. The stems of these grasses are used for food for farm animals.

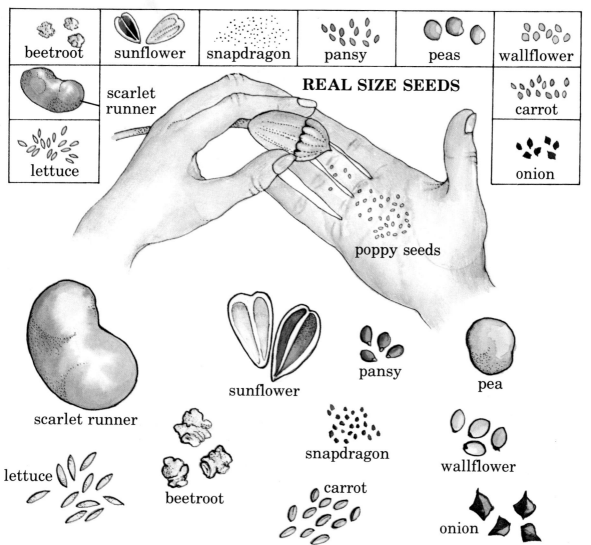

beetroot	sunflower	snapdragon	pansy	peas	wallflower

REAL SIZE SEEDS

scarlet runner

carrot

lettuce

onion

poppy seeds

scarlet runner

sunflower

pansy

pea

lettuce

beetroot

snapdragon

carrot

wallflower

onion

Some seeds are large. Some seeds are small. You cannot tell how big the plant will be by looking at the size of the seed.

19

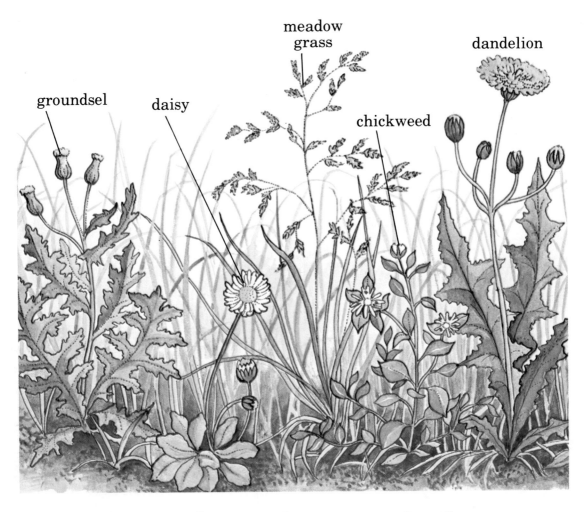

groundsel

daisy

meadow
grass

chickweed

dandelion

These plants often grow in the
garden. We do not plant them there.
We do not want them in our garden.
When a plant grows where it is not
wanted, we call it a weed.

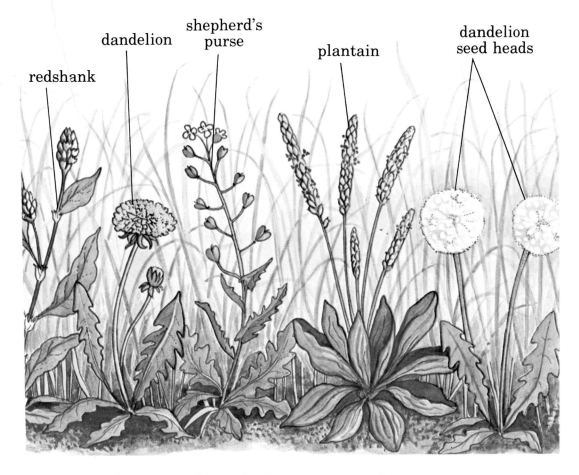

redshank   dandelion   shepherd's purse   plantain   dandelion seed heads

    The seeds of these weeds are carried here. The birds carry some. The wind blows some around. The flowers attract the bees. The bees carry pollen from one flower to another. This makes more seeds and more weeds.

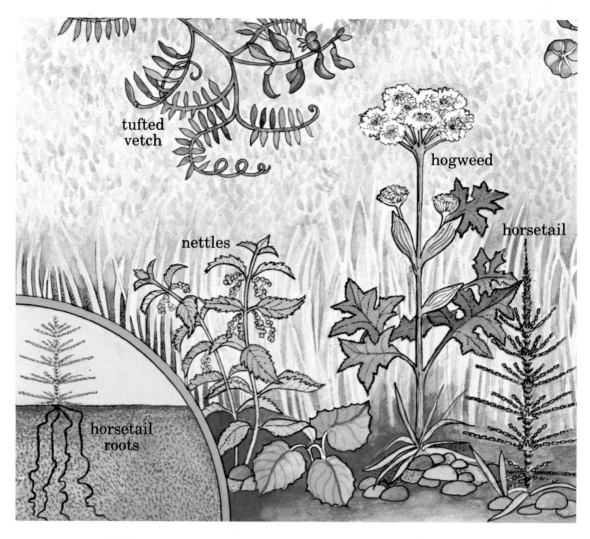

tufted
vetch

hogweed

horsetail

nettles

horsetail
roots

We plant grass along roads. The
grass is pretty. The grass helps hold
the soil in place. Many weeds grow
along the roadside also. They
sometimes kill the grass.

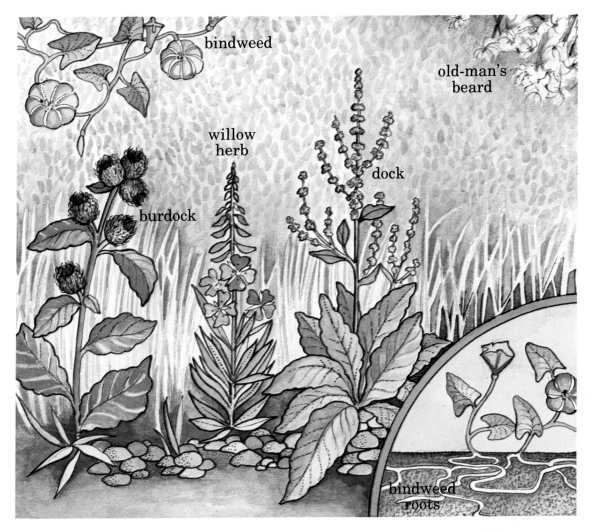

bindweed

old-man's beard

willow herb

dock

burdock

bindweed roots

The roots of weeds are strong. They can grow deep into the soil to find water. Horsetail roots are black. Bindweed roots are white.

ragwort

spear thistle

creeping thistle

yellow rattle

meadow buttercup

creeping buttercup

Sometimes it is hard to tell which plants are weeds. If you decide to look at the roots of weeds, make sure that they are weeds before pulling them up.

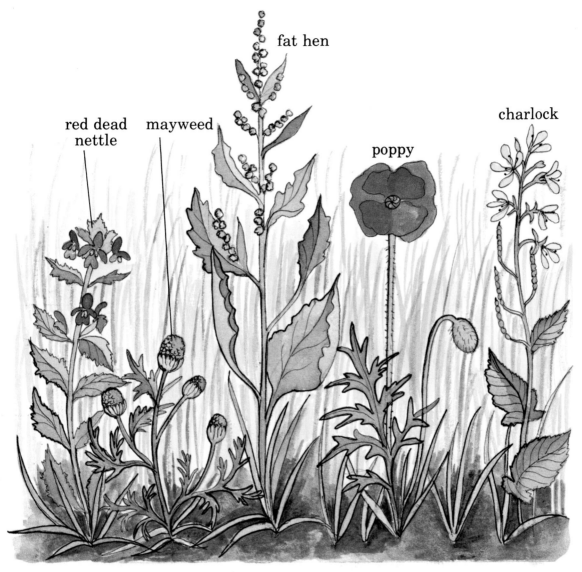

red dead nettle

mayweed

fat hen

poppy

charlock

Some people plant poppies in a flower garden. They have beautiful flowers. They will grow every year without being planted again.

dandelion

maple
keys

You may have picked a dandelion
seed head. The girl in the picture did.
She blew on it. She is helping the
seeds travel. The wind blows seeds to
new places. This is why you may see
a tiny maple tree growing when there
is no big tree nearby.

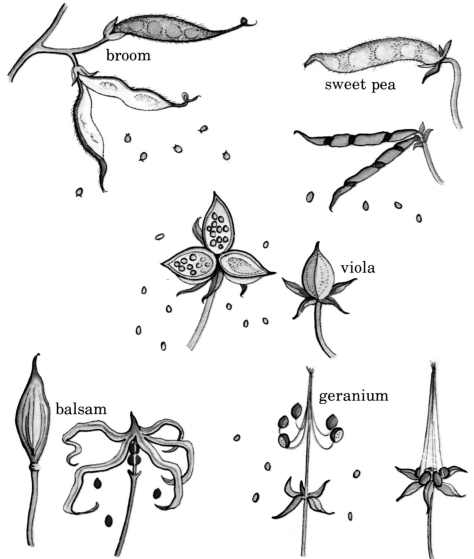

broom

sweet pea

viola

balsam

geranium

All seeds do not blow in the wind. Some seeds are in pods like the pods of peas. The seed pod dries out in the fall. The pod will pop open. The seeds will be thrown out. Sometimes birds will pick them up and carry them far away.

27

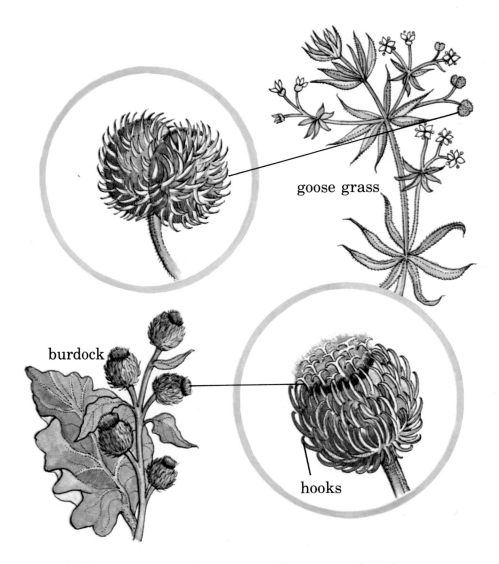

goose grass

burdock

hooks

These seeds travel in a different way. Each seed case has hooks. It will hook onto an animal as the animal passes by. It will fall off later in a new place.

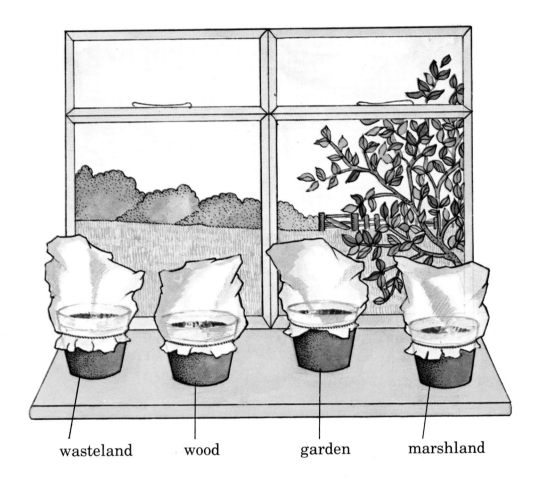

wasteland   wood   garden   marshland

There are many seeds in the soil. Some children collected soil from different places. They put the soil in four pots. They did not plant any seeds in the soil. They put the pots in the window for sunlight. Plants will grow in all of them.

What I Know About Seeds and Weeds

We eat some seeds for food.

Seeds must be dried before they will grow.

Plants must not be too close together, or they will not be strong.

The plant will grow no matter how the seed is put into the ground.

The privet and nightshade plants are poisonous.

Do not eat berries or nuts unless you know they are safe.

People plant gardens in the spring.

Seeds from grasses that are used as foods are called grains.

Farm animals and people eat grains.

A plant that grows where it is not wanted is called a weed.

Seeds are carried from place to place by bees, birds, and the wind.

Grass helps hold soil in place.

Can You Answer These Questions?

1. Do seeds have to be dried before they will grow?

2. What happens if you put too many seeds in a pot?

3. If a seed is upside down in the ground, will the plant grow?

4. When do people plant gardens?

5. How long will beans live without soil?

6. Who eats grains?

7. Can you tell how big a plant will be by the size of the seed?

8. What do you call plants that grow where you do not want them to?

9. How are seeds carried from place to place?

10. What will happen if you put soil in a pot in the sunlight?

ANSWERS

1. Yes.
2. The plants will not be strong and healthy.
3. Yes.
4. In the spring.
5. Several days.
6. Farm animals and people.
7. No.
8. Weeds.
9. By birds, bees, and the wind.
10. Plants will grow.

31

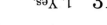

Words in SEEDS and WEEDS

seed
page 4

grain
page 18

pit
page 5

seed pod
page 27

roots
page 15

seed case
page 28

shoots
page 15

hooks
page 28